The Collection
2023

compiled by John Field

EXPRESS NEWSPAPERS

 CASSELL

First published in Great Britain in 2022 by Cassell,
a division of Octopus Publishing Group Ltd, Carmelite House,
50 Victoria Embankment, London EC4Y 0DZ
www.octopusbooks.co.uk

An Hachette UK Company
www.hachette.co.uk

Cartoons

British Cartoon Archive

Cartoons supplied by British Cartoon Archive
Cartoons compiled by John Field

ISBN 978 1 78840 356 6

A CIP catalogue record for this book is available from the British Library.

Printed and bound in China

10 9 8 7 6 5 4 3 2 1

Contents

The first sighting of the Giles family, on 5 August 1945.

The Giles Family

This year's collection of Giles's cartoons has been chosen to bring together probably the two best-known and well-loved families in the country: the royal family and the Giles family.

Regarding the former, Giles was "a kind of cartooning jester to the royal family" as recorded on page 160 of this collection. Also recorded on the same page is the rather charming comment to Giles from the Queen's Press Secretary, relating to a specific cartoon, saying, "Her Majesty requests today's cartoon to commemorate one of her husband's most glorious indiscretions", illustrating the warmth with which his work was regarded by members of the royal family. This is further shown by the fact that, a few weeks after this cartoon appeared, Giles was invited to a "small informal luncheon party" at Buckingham Palace with the Queen and Prince Philip. By the time Giles retired, the royal family had acquired more than 40 of his original drawings, with the largest number being held by Prince Philip.

Regarding the Giles family cartoons, last year's collection showed them against the backdrop of their natural habitat – the family home – room by room. This year, we look at them again, but this time through a range of family activities – enjoying (or enduring) meal times, watching TV, in the garden and on holiday. As usual, the scenes are frequently hectic and, not surprisingly, Grandma is often the source of trouble. However, on occasions her grandson, Ernie, plays a key role but manages somehow to make it less obvious.

Although Giles sought to entertain his audience by finding humour in most aspects of British everyday life, he also used his cartoons to comment upon more serious matters. He had the ability to approach these difficult issues in a way that made them acceptable subjects for a cartoon. I believe that Giles learnt this skill while working as a cartoonist throughout the Second World War. This ability is recognised in the catalogue which accompanied an exhibition of some of his war cartoons, held in Brussels in 1994 to celebrate the 50th anniversary of the liberation of Belgium by British forces. Charles Dierick, the Artistic Director of the Belgian Centre for Cartoon Art at that time, stated: "Giles, with his devastating sense of humour and great comic power, was Winston Churchill's secret weapon on the home front as well as on the battlegrounds of Europe". This was the period when Giles truly developed his individual style and his work became increasingly well known. It is pertinent to note that when the editor of the *Express* newspaper sent Giles to join the troops in Europe as a war cartoonist in September 1944, he said,

"Your cartoons have done so much for morale both here and amongst the troops – just think what affect they would have if you were actually out there".

The end of the war in Europe in May 1945 meant his established source of wartime events and characters also ran dry. Soon after, on 5 August, his cartoon family appeared for the first time, complete with Grandma (see page 6). This appearance was the inception of the family that would become a major and regular feature of Giles's cartoons for the rest of his career.

The introduction of the Giles family gave the cartoonist a vehicle through which to explore the effects of events on the world stage through the eyes of everyday folk in the UK. It enabled him to extend the gentle approach that he'd taken when dealing with the seriousness of his wartime subject matter to all the vagaries of post-war life, however sensitive or difficult they were in reality. This gift is best illustrated by the following cartoons, all involving the Giles family, which feature in this year's collection.

1 February 1955 (Meal Times): At this time, there was grave concern in the West about the threat of invasion to Taiwan by the People's Republic of China. Grandma's bizarre reaction back in the UK is used by Giles to make a reference to this worrying, but distant, situation.

17 July 1955 (On Holiday): Urgent questions were being asked in Parliament about the likely shortage of coal in the coming winter. Giles set his comment on the subject on a beach, with a blazing sun, in contrast to the bleak prospect of a cold winter without fuel.

31 October 1961 (Watching TV): The West had just received the news that the Soviet Union had tested the world's largest nuclear weapon. Giles comments upon this very worrying development by using his favourite character, Grandma, and her digestive system to lighten the mood.

21 July 1966 (Meal Times): This was a period of major financial problems in the UK, with Leader of the Opposition Edward Heath saying in Parliament, "There can be no mistaking the gravity of the economic situation which we are debating this afternoon". On this occasion, Giles uses Father's over-the-top behaviour to comment on this very difficult national situation.

1 August 1968 (In the Garden): Giles is referring to the impending threat of four Warsaw Pact countries invading Czechoslovakia to prevent it moving towards greater independence from the Soviet bloc. His only reference in the cartoon to this momentous world event, however, appears in small print on Vera's newspaper.

12 July 1970 (In the Garden): An anticipated food shortage due to a strike by dock workers led to many people finding extreme solutions to the problem. Giles shows one possible but outrageous strategy, again by featuring Grandma up to one of her petty criminal tricks.

22 September 1972 (In the Garden): At this period a large number of letter bombs were sent from Amsterdam to Israeli embassies around the world, many signed by a group calling itself Black September. Grandma's extreme and typically selfish response to the situation is used by the cartoonist to address this appalling act of terrorism.

26 January 1976 (Meal Times): This period was known as the third Cod War, as the British fishing fleet, working near Iceland, was threatened by Icelandic gunboats. Again, Giles uses Grandma, along with one of the family's furry pets, to make a light reference to this unfortunate conflict.

2 October 1986 (Watching TV): This was during a long tense period when the two main world powers, the USA and USSR, were in theory at peace, but at the same time participating in an aggressive arms race and ideological bids for world dominance. Giles's reference to a hugely important meeting between the leaders of these two countries was to have Grandma linking it to the goings-on in a very popular and widely-watched TV soap opera.

20 October 1987 (In the Garden): This cartoon refers to a violent cyclone in Britain that occurred on the night of 15–16 October, with hurricane-force winds causing considerable damage across the country. Giles commented on the resulting destruction by showing indefatigable Grandma managing to make a small income from the family's neighbours by sweeping up a few leaves.

Weaving these serious events into the lives of the British public with sympathy and humour is part of Giles's unique skill and the Giles family proved to be an invaluable tool through which to do this. I hope that readers will enjoy this year's collection of Giles's insight into world events through the lives of Britain's two best-known families.

John Field

Meal Times

I am not sure that Mother is happy to hear this.

"I heard Dad tell Mr. Smith that he's going to buy Mum a lovely set of new tyres for the car for Christmas."

Daily Express, 22 December 1953

Grandma, often the first in the family to react to world events, is greatly concerned by a deteriorating situation regarding the threat of invasion in Taiwan, formerly known as Formosa, by the People's Republic of China. The Formosa Resolution, 1955, gave the US President the authority "to employ the Armed Forces of the United States as he deems necessary for the specific purpose of securing and protecting Formosa and the Pescadores against armed attack".

"I'm sure war's not as imminent as all that, Grandma."

Daily Express, 1 February 1955

12   The younger members of the family are delighted by their luck and have quickly taken to the joys of owning a pony. Even George, the family's eldest son, who is normally shown with his head in a book, has come to life and is bringing in some straw for the newcomer. However, some of the older members of the family are not so sure. Grandma ignores the whole thing, being engrossed in the 1955 International Trophy motor race due to be held at Silverstone two days after this cartoon appeared. Of course, Giles himself was an avid supporter of motor racing, taking part in his own Jaguar XK120 roadster.

"I can't think of anything this family wanted more than to win a pony."

Daily Express, 5 May 1955

Giles, who had no children of his own, often took pleasure in showing how the innocence of childhood can be so direct. Note the US serviceman near the window – the cartoonist had many friends amongst these "Friendly Invasion" troops during the Cold War when many thousands were stationed in Suffolk. It was not unusual for him to include one in a cartoon, usually along with the serviceman's girlfriend from the local area.

13

"She's not as pretty as the waitress who served us at the Food Fair."

Daily Express, 30 August 1956

The Ides is roughly the middle of a month and was notable in Roman times as a deadline for settling debts. In 44 BC, it became notorious as the date of the assassination of Julius Caesar, which made the Ides of March a turning point in Roman history. Ernie is simply pointing out an interesting fact.

"Today's the Ides of March."

Daily Express, 15 March 1957

John Dryden became England's first Poet Laureate in 1668. Despite the virtues of country life referred to by Dryden, Giles manages to include the many perils facing those who venture into the English countryside. His cartoon includes an approaching thunder storm, a fire which will not light in the required location but manages, nevertheless, to spread elsewhere, an advancing column of killer ants and swarms of flying biting insects, an essential piece of picnicking equipment which has been left at home and the imminent danger of an escaped bull.

"How blessed is he who leads a country life, Unvexed with anxious cares, and void of strife!" – DRYDEN (1631–1700)

Daily Express, 9 July 1958

16

The day before, Ipswich Town Football Club lost 2–5 at home against Luton Town in the 5th round of the F.A. Cup. Giles, an avid supporter of Ipswich Town, is obviously using Father to express his own feelings on the game.

"Anyone would think WE let that blessed goal through that put your team out of the Cup."

Sunday Express, 15 February 1959

That evening, the Miss World contest was held at the Lyceum Ballroom in London and won by Corine Spier-Rottschäfer, a Dutch model and beauty queen. It is not recorded if Young Ernie was, in fact, on the judging panel and, if so, how he voted.

"For you, Einstein – as you were able to tell them England wasn't a Pacific island in their Quiz last week, ITV want you to judge the Miss World contest tonight."

Daily Express, 10 November 1959

Grandma, no stranger to the use of dirty tricks, obviously ensured that she was the only one in the family to back the actual winner of that year's Derby.

Angry Silence. Grandma tipped everybody also-rans but backed the winner herself.

Daily Express, 2 June 1960

That afternoon at Wimbledon, a young Christine Truman was playing Maria Bueno of Brazil in the Ladies Singles semi-final. Bueno, a pre-eminent player who was ranked No 1 in the world in 1959, 1960, 1964 and 1966, won in three sets. Most of the family members are showing justifiable signs of deep concern about Christine's chances against such a formidable opponent.

"How many of you playing this Christine Truman match this afternoon?"

Daily Express, 30 June 1960

20 That year's Miss World contest was won, on the day before, by Jamaican Carole Joan Crawford – the first winning delegate from the Caribbean. Father appears to be unhappy – perhaps because he is unlucky with his football pools. Or maybe it is Giles again expressing his displeasure with his beloved team, Ipswich, having been beaten 3–1 away by Nottingham Forest on the previous day. I suspect that the young entrepreneur Ernie is expanding his business empire by charging parking fees for the family's pets and the other children's toys.

"Good morning, Miss World."

Sunday Express, 3 November 1963

"Which do you think we'll get first – 'If-cigarettes-go-up-I'm-giving-up-smoking' or 'If-beer-goes-up-I'm-giving-up-drinking'?"

Daily Express, 14 April 1964

22 Giles loved to celebrate the British habit of being overtaken by our country's changeable weather. He also often liked to include one of his vehicles in a cartoon – here we see his Land Rover, registration LRT 140. Father is simply pointing out that, having reached the Summer Solstice, winter and Christmas will now be getting nearer. Is it just coincidental that Giles shows Grandma, with her many irritating habits, being "treated" by a Pest Control vehicle?

"That's your father – always looking on the bright side – 'Do we realise that from today the nights start drawing in and we'll soon be thinking about Christmas cards.'"

Sunday Express, 21 June 1964

It is surprising that Father is in such a bad mood with England beating France 2–0 the day before in the 1966 Football World Cup tournament. This, of course, led to them winning the cup nine days later by beating Germany 4–2. The clue, however, is in his newspaper headline, which refers to the dire situation relating to the United Kingdom's financial situation at that time, with Prime Minister Harold Wilson threatening a tough package of deflation and austerity.

"Now say Sorry to Teddy for knocking him off the table – it's not his fault we've got another crisis."

Daily Express, 21 July 1966

24 Although the family usually embraces new members of all varieties, it is obvious that this one is not particularly welcome. I can understand Grandma's dislike as she probably fears the bird, with its raucous voice, as a potential competitor in family debates, in which she generally dominates.

"What's roast mynah bird taste like, Dad?"

Daily Express, 29 December 1966

Two days before this cartoon appeared, a British driver was breathalysed by police for the very first time, suspected of driving whilst under the influence of alcohol. Father has obviously taken this as a warning and Mother, ever optimistic, feels that she can see an improvement in his early morning demeanour as a result.

"I think he's nicer in the mornings since he gave up drinking."

Daily Express, 10 October 1967

The BBC TV programme, *The Forsyte Saga*, about an upper middle class family in Victorian and Edwardian England, was extremely popular at this time. Soames Forsyte was a major character in the programme and it had been trailed that he would die that evening. Even the family pets appear distressed.

"Welcome to our Sunday Entertainments Department – Soames Forsyte kicks the bucket tonight."

Sunday Express, 2 March 1969

It was reported that Princess Anne had shocked people during a visit to Australia by using a phrase worthy of her father, Prince Philip. Mother takes the opportunity to make a point regarding something which possibly troubles her.

27

"Like some of them in this house – she picks it up from her father."

Daily Express, 2 April 1970

This cartoon celebrates the return of national newspapers after a four-day strike by printers. Mother is not sure that she welcomes it.

"I preferred the news on the radio and TV – they forget it in five minutes. With newspapers they've still got the evidence."
(Postscript to the newspaper strike)

Sunday Express, 14 June 1970

Obviously the BBC's Wonderful Radio One specialism is modern music and the current chart lists was not Grandma's cup of tea. It is also obvious that Father (and, I strongly suspect, Giles) were in full agreement with her and probably not really in favour of the popularity of transistor radios in general.

"Off transistors! Nothing puts Grandma in her let's-hang-everybody mood quicker than Wonderful Radio One."

Sunday Express, 17 October 1971

Father has tried this one before – see the cartoon from 22 December 1953 (see page 10). On this occasion, Mother waited 35 days before getting her revenge.

"You may remember you bought me a spare tyre for the car on Mother's Day."

Daily Express, 17 June 1973

George Best was a very popular and successful Manchester United footballer, who had walked out of the team partway through the previous season. It had just been announced that he had been persuaded to return but, unfortunately, his return only lasted a few weeks and his contract was cancelled the following season. Obviously Grandma had her own views about him.

"That wasn't a very nice thing to say, Grandma – 'About the weight of his head.'"

Daily Express, 11 September 1973

32 At this time, the world was experiencing a serious lack of paper due to a shortage of wood pulp. It would appear that the children are hoping to help by re-using Father's newspaper to make toilet paper. Father may not fully welcome their commendable, but possibly pre-emptory, efforts to help the situation.

"You're good boys to think of paper saving, but I don't think daddy will like you cutting up his paper before he's read it."

Daily Express, 22 January 1974

Giles's team, Ipswich Town, had drawn 0–0 at home against Leeds United the day before in the F.A. Cup quarter finals. I suspect that this influenced his chosen theme for marking Mother's Day on this occasion.

"In the fever and excitement of yesterday's F.A. quarter finals, I hope you all remembered the Mother's Day flowers."

Sunday Express, 9 March 1975

34   This was a period of mounting tensions between British fishing trawlers and Icelandic gunboats over fishing rights in the North Atlantic, known as the Cod Wars.

"Grandma, with a grave international crisis over the future of cod you're not supposed to give yours to the cat."

Daily Express, 26 January 1976

On this day, Ronald Reagan was inaugurated as the 40th president of the United States. Obviously Grandma was an ardent supporter. *The Hitch-Hiker's Guide to the Galaxy* was a comedy science-fiction novel, which became a multi-media international hit – maybe Ernie felt Grandma looked more like an alien space traveller.

"Grandma is playing 'Statue of Liberty' not 'Hitch-Hiker's Guide to the Galaxy!"

Daily Express, 20 January 1981

36 Three days before this cartoon appeared, it was widely reported that the musician Prince may have let slip a strong swear word during his debut musical performance on *Saturday Night Live*, an American late-night TV show. This is one of a series of Giles's cartoons having Grandma's pet parrot as a major character in family life. On this occasion, it was obviously expressing strong views on touchy subjects in very colourful language. However, so far as Grandma is concerned, it can do no wrong.

"If you wish to remain a permanent member of this family – no politics or religion!"

Daily Express, 24 February 1981

In his cartoons, Giles often expressed the view that the festive period meant nothing but a great deal of hard work to the women of the household. Grandma's pet parrot is up to one of its usual tricks and the family's younger members are being kept out of trouble.

"My Happy New Year will begin when the decorations and the last mince pie are down and not before."

Sunday Express, 2 January 1983

38 This was a period of unrest in the mining industry with many miners threatening to strike. Eventually, there was a year-long strike in 1984. It involved considerable hardship for miners and general violence in one of the most bitter industrial disputes Britain has ever seen.

"That was very rude to tell Aunty that a couple of weeks at the coalface would make her think differently about the miners' strike."

Sunday Express, 6 March 1983

Grandma, a great lover of the horses and fond of a flutter is, on the face of it, concerned about the future of Aintree Race Course, the home of the internationally famous Grand National. A scheme was being considered to develop the site for housing and a campaign was established to save the race course. Generous donations allowed the Jockey Club to acquire Aintree and secure its future for horse racing. However, Ernie's suspicions about Grandma's intentions may be well-founded.

"What's the betting Aintree doesn't see a penny of it?"

Daily Express, 12 April 1983

40 Three days earlier, Margaret Thatcher's Conservative Party had won the General Election with a landslide majority of 144 seats. In the light of the country's difficult economic situation at that time, she made it clear that she was considering introducing a wide range of drastic financial cuts. There is little doubt that Butch the dog is going to benefit from Father's mistake.

"I hope the Prime Minister makes a better job of her carving than your father."

Sunday Express, 12 June 1983

In addition to his pleasure in drawing large crowds of people, Giles also loved to capture the chaos which usually reigned in the family's kitchen in the run-up to Christmas. The twins are enthralled with the sausages, Butch is delighted at Father's return, Grandma is about to be angry, Vera is, as usual, unhappy and Mother is just too busy to concern herself with their visitor who seems quite happy sampling her mince pies washed down with a swig of bubbly.

"I don't know who he is – he called and said 'I'm Father Christmas' and he's been here all afternoon."

Daily Express, 24 December 1983

42 "National Smile Week", now "National Smile Month", is one of the largest dental health events in Europe. It is organised by the Oral Health Foundation, a UK-based charity, and promotes the benefits of having good oral health and the value of a healthy smile. I have the feeling that for most of the Giles family it would have been difficult to retain a smile for a week, let alone a month.

"Off smiles, everyone! National Smile Week is over, in case you didn't know."

Sunday Express, 20 May 1984

Another cartoon illustrating total chaos in the family's kitchen just before Christmas but this time Mother has her "Get out of Jail" card.

"Noel! I've just won a Christmas holiday for one in the Bahamas – plane leaves tonight!"

Daily Express, 20 December 1984

44 Two days earlier, former Member of Parliament Jeffrey Archer had been awarded libel damages of £500,000 plus costs from the *Star* newspaper, which had accused him of paying a prostitute for sex. I am not sure whether Grandma felt that he had been unfairly rewarded by the court or whether she thought that half a million was insufficient to cover the gravity of the crime.

"Grandma, can we have breakfast without your verdict on the Archer verdict?"

Sunday Express, 26 July 1987

This cartoon gives the impression that Shrove Tuesday can be a dangerous time to be in the Giles family household with Mother effectively using pancakes as a weapon, or is it just that she has a poor aim? This was a period of intense discussions between French President François Mitterrand and British Prime Minister Margaret Thatcher, over differences in economic and defence policies. There is no record available of the actual words used in these discussions.

"Grandma! The French Premier swearing at Mrs. Thatcher does not mean you can use that word in front of the children."

Daily Express, 16 February 1988

Sadly it appears that this is the normal situation on Mother's Day in this family.

"Now we come to the bit where Father's come out without any money and Mother pays."

Sunday Express, 13 March 1988

The initial concept of the Jaguar XJ220, a two-seater sports car, was unveiled at the British International Motor Show held in Birmingham at the time of this cartoon but it did not enter into production until 1992 at a price of £470,000. Just 275 of these cars were produced between that year and 1994. Giles was always a great lover of fast cars and he himself owned and raced a 1951 XK120 Jaguar roadster which appeared in a number of his cartoons.

"If you're planning on a new family car remember I shall be casting a vote."

Daily Express, 20 October 1988

48 Two days earlier, the BBC had broadcast a star-studded evening of entertainment, introduced by Terry Wogan, Sue Cook and Joanna Lumley, as the climax of its annual appeal to raise money for Children in Need. It is obvious that everyone in the room suspects Grandma. It is also clear that Giles supported the appeal by including Pudsey Bear within the family group.

"The BBC wants to verify the Children in Need bid for tickets to Disneyland at £2,000 a head."

Sunday Express, 20 November 1988

"Mixing the BBC's Royal Variety Show canned applause with Prince Philip's End of the World forecast certainly helps."

Daily Express, 29 November 1988

Watching TV

The national economic situation was not good, with large increases in unemployment and short-time working being discussed at Westminster. Obviously, the family could not see a great deal to laugh about at the time.

"If they do put the day-to-day proceedings of the House of Commons on television we shall be able to see what causes so many parliamentary reports to be followed by the phrase: 'There was laughter.'"

Daily Express, 5 February 1959

This was a week before the General Election so the speech was probably a political broadcast by a politician. Grandma has made clear her thoughts on whatever was said.

"I didn't think it was such a bad speech as all that, Grandma."

Daily Express, 1 October 1959

52   No doubt Father would rather see the end of his cowboy programme, but at least there appears to be a lot of help available from the children.

"I like the way they always ask you if you'd LIKE to help them with the decorations."

Sunday Express, 20 December 1959

This was the first day of the Olympic Games, held in Rome. Understandably Father is upset when one of the children (or is it, in fact, Grandma), turns over to a very popular cowboy serial starring Clint Eastwood, being shown at the same time.

"Next one who switches *RAWHIDE* on in the middle of my Olympic Games – BED!"

Daily Express, 25 August 1960

54   Father had made it clear that he was not interested in the American elections. With significant changes taking place in British homes in terms of attitudes and lifestyles at that time, teachers were discussing the impact this had upon a child's education. It is apparent that the twins are bright enough to quickly spot an opportunity when it arises.

"Dad, what's it worth if I don't tell teacher you and Grandma just used a rude little word?"

Daily Express, 8 November 1960

The day before, the largest nuclear weapon ever constructed to date, the "Tzar Bomba", was set off by the Soviet Union in the Russian Arctic Sea, producing a seismic shock wave equivalent to an earthquake of over 5.0 on the Richter Scale.

"That wasn't a fifty-megatoner or an earthquake – that was Grandma's tummy rumbling."

Daily Express, 31 October 1961

During the FIFA World Cup that year, the whole of England got behind the national team, who went on to win the tournament by beating West Germany 4–2 in the final on 30 July.

"Well how about that for a family who's been moaning for a month about too much World Cup."

Daily Express, 14 July 1966

Ernie, the organiser as usual, is explaining to his neighbour Stinker the arrangements the family makes for the two-week Wimbledon TV onslaught, with sufficient seats, nourishment and drinks. The seating arrangement is also carefully worked out but, knowing Grandma's sense of self-importance within the family hierarchy, I do not think that she will accept her poor view of the screen for very long. Adequate provision is also made for restraining Father, who usually has a poor opinion of the whole event, for causing too much disturbance.

"All set for a fortnight's Wimbledon seige – Dad, Mum, Vera, Grandma..."

Sunday Express, 25 June 1967

58   The annual mono TV licence at that time was £5 and the previous January, a licence for colour TV had been introduced for the first time at £10. On the day this cartoon appeared, there was considerable public anger at the Government debating a £1 increase in the cost of a colour TV licence.

"What's the betting they all wake up and say that programme wasn't worth an extra pound on the licence?"

Daily Express, 25 July 1968

At this time, the US Apollo astronauts were on their way to landing on the moon, which took place three days later. Many people were glued to the TV throughout this period and, no doubt, the family's normal routine was disrupted.

"Kindly inform your mother that Earth Man is home and wants his tea."

Daily Express, 17 July 1969

60 The FIFA World Cup tournament was taking place in Mexico that year. Father was obviously looking forward to the match, due to start in 10 minutes time, but I have a feeling his plans were thwarted. It was Mexico versus the USSR and ended in a 2–2 draw.

"Now who's going to tell him Uncle Ernie and Auntie Rosie and the children are coming to tea?"

Sunday Express, 31 May 1970

I suspect that Mother is successfully winding up certain members of her family; Father and eldest son, George, look particularly aggrieved.

"I see they're putting on a Party Political Broadcast instead of Macbeth on Christmas night, and running Macbeth instead of Football on Boxing Day."

Sunday Express, 12 November 1972

62 *Tom and Jerry* was a very popular American animation shown on British TV at this time. It featured the rivalry between Tom the cat, and Jerry the mouse. This cartoon suggests that their continuation on TV in Britain had been uncertain.

"Relax! We haven't got to emigrate to the States after all. Tom and Jerry have got a reprieve."

Daily Express, 8 December 1972

In the FIFA World Cup being played in West Germany, Scotland did not get past the second round, unfortunately for Grandma's 63
sister. England failed to qualify for the tournament.

"Dad, why do we have to have 'Scotland the Brave' all through breakfast just because Grandma's got a wee sister in Aberdeen?"

Daily Express, 25 June 1974

Young Ernie seems quite happy to watch the family's Supreme Champion destroy the Aunt's shoe.

"The Supreme Champion of this house has just eaten one of Auntie Ivy's shoes."

Sunday Express, 9 February 1975

The Bay City Rollers were a Scottish band that achieved global success during this period. The United Kingdom European Communities membership referendum was a public vote on whether the UK should remain a member of the European Community, which was held two days after this cartoon appeared. More than 67% voted to remain.

"Somehow our Referendum Voters section seems to lack the enthusiasm of our Bay City Rollers section."

Daily Express, 3 June 1975

66 I suspect that this survey is really part of a campaign by the children of the family, master-minded by Ernie, to get more food for themselves.

"Butch's breakfast menu: Two cotton reels, Grandma's slippers, 1oz. Dad's tobacco, one *Daily Express*, half-shovel coal, half-hundredweight Bonio – yes, I suppose you could say pets eat more than children."

Daily Express, 23 September 1975

The next day, announcing his budget, Chancellor Denis Healey told the nation that for once he was "not asking for anyone to make sacrifices", instead offering £2,400 million in tax cuts to stimulate the economy. The twins have already got their piggy banks ready but it seems that Butch just does not like the look of Mr. Healey despite what he is saying.

"Shut up, Butch, wait till we see what he does tomorrow."

Daily Express, 10 April 1978

The 1978 FIFA World Cup was being held in Argentina and the host nation won, beating the Netherlands 3–1 in the final. England, again, failed to qualify but the men of the Giles household still avidly followed the matches.

"Let there be no moaning at the bar when our Wimbledon fortnight comes round."

Daily Express, 9 June 1978

Dame Margot Fonteyn had been for 45 years, the Royal Ballet's prima ballerina before retiring that month at the age of 60. Grandma is speaking, of course, from a position of extreme old age.

"This girl Fonteyn could do well if she sticks at it."

Daily Express, 6 November 1979

70   At this time, the BBC was facing increased competition from the commercial sector and the Corporation began looking for savings. Vera's initiative is well-meaning but unlikely to survive the next major sporting event. However, with the switching off of the TV, members of the family have rediscovered other pursuits including knitting, cards, reading, tidying up and gardening; and I think that Ernie and the twins have taken the opportunity to make some money by providing drinks and cakes.

"Vera thinks she's helping the BBC save its £130 million by not switching it on."

Sunday Express, 2 March 1980

Selina Scott and Debbie Rix appeared regularly on the *Breakfast Time* programme and became extremely popular, particularly amongst the men.

"You'll have to start getting to bed earlier to get down in time to see your Debbie and Selina."

Daily Express, 18 January 1983

72 *Breakfast Time* was Britain's first national breakfast television programme, broadcast from 17 January 1983 until 29 September 1989. The programme started at 6.30 am and its relatively easy style quickly made it very popular.

"Dad, I've just counted up – we've got six more people than we've got in the family."

Daily Express, 1 February 1983

With the threat of a TV black-out affecting Ascot, Wimbledon and football, a lot of people are going to be very unhappy.

"Remember the days when all the males in this house had a fortnight's moan if we switched Wimbledon on?"

Sunday Express, 19 June 1983

74 "Video Nasty" is a term that refers to low-budget horror and exploitative films, criticised by the press and social commentators for their violent content. Earlier in 1983, the Department of Public Prosecutions had compiled a list of 72 such video releases which were successfully prosecuted and banned. I am not sure that Grandma and poor little Vera quite fit into this category.

"That's the kind of video nasty I'd ban from the home – two reels of Grandma and Vera paddling in Benidorm."

Sunday Express, 13 November 1983

"She's still in an uncontrollable rage over the babbling BBC commentators for ruining her snooker tournament."

Daily Express, 31 January 1984

76   The Olympic Games that year were held in Los Angeles, which with the time difference, meant a lot of midnight TV viewing for Father. Perseus was a Greek hero and Tessa Sanderson, a six-time British Olympian winning the Gold Medal in javelin for Great Britain that year. It would appear that Father has precisely 15 minutes to get to the station.

"Awake, Perseus – if you can go as fast as Tessa Sanderson's javelin, you might just catch the 7.10."

Daily Express, 9 August 1984

Of course, the new *Star Wars* video was a prized acquisition, but selling Baby George to fund it is a bit extreme.

"Whether we can afford the new *Star Wars* video depends on how much we can get for him on the baby market."

Daily Express, 25 August 1984

78 Obviously Grandma's Scottish sister is down visiting for Hogmanay, along with a number of other elderly relatives. Eldest son and bookworm George is trying to finish George Orwell's *1984* before the end of the year and Stinker is up to his usual tricks with Baby George. It is unlikely that the television message will attract much attention but the general calm of those assembled is about to be rudely disturbed by you know who.

"Hoots everybody! Grandma and her sister are back from their Over Sixties Hogmanay party."

Daily Express, 31 December 1984

Mother's comment refers to a BBC TV programme popular and obviously relates to a relationship that fails. The message on the screen refers to a summit meeting between the leaders of the US and the USSR, planned to start nine days later in Reykjavik, Iceland. Obviously, Grandma does not have high hopes for the success of this high-level meeting.

"Don't be so pessimistic, Grandma – not everything on TV ends with one of them standing the other one up at the altar."
(Headline – *Eastenders'* Michelle jilts Lofty)

Daily Express, 2 October 1986

80 The day before, AFC Wimbledon unexpectedly beat the league champions Liverpool 1–0 at Wembley to win the F.A. Cup. The win has obviously encouraged Ernie to improve his goal-scoring skills, with George Junior in goal, but Father's friends do not seem to be in a good mood.

"Tell Daddy some gentlemen are here to see him about the 50–1 Wimbledon to win the Cup he was giving them yesterday."

Sunday Express, 15 May 1988

Giles made no secret of his dislike of any form of football hooliganism and he is making the point strongly in this cartoon. The country was preparing for a football match between England and the USSR on 18 June, which the USSR won 3–1. Unfortunately, at the time, an element of the Chelsea supporters had a reputation for bad behaviour. At the same time Gorbachev in Moscow was introducing a more peaceful policy of Glasnost, aimed at opening up the Soviet Union.

"It's keep Chelsea out of Moscow or bye-bye Glasnost."

Daily Express, 31 May 1988

In the Garden

The first National Baby Week was held in 1917, during the First World War, with the slogan: "It is more dangerous to be an infant in England than to be a soldier in France". It aimed at improving the health of newborn babies, pointing out that in 1915, "nine soldiers had died every hour at the front, while twelve babies died at home". Both figures are, of course, frightening.

"That's a nice thing to call baby on the first day of National Baby Week."

Sunday Express, 13 June 1954

Through the late 1950s and first half of the 1960s, skirts got shorter, epitomising the increasing freedom of the period with rock 'n' roll, a general feeling of optimism and the emancipation of women. I am not convinced that Ernie needed to worry too much.

"If Grandma's bought a short dress I'm going to leave home."

Daily Express, 31 January 1958

Obviously Father will regret his decision but the children, no doubt, are pleased with these additions to the family's collection of pets.

"So much for Father's idea that the children were old enough to go to the zoo by themselves this year."

Daily Express, 26 May 1958

"Seven, six, five, four, three, two..."

Sunday Express, 26 October 1958

A teachers' strike was threatened over pay and Father, aided by Grandma, is taking precautions just in case.

"Assuming their teachers do go on strike and we've got to have them at home a few more weeks..."

Sunday Express, 9 April 1961

"It was a nice party until someone asked Grandma 'What about Quintin Hogg?'"

Sunday Express, 25 July 1965

Think about it.

"He spent all his holiday painting the name on his boat – I hadn't the heart to tell him."

Daily Express, 12 April 1966

The miniskirt was regarded as the defining female style of the 1960s but it took until 1966 for skirts to become really short, at seven inches above the knee. It is not clear whether Grandma has ordered these modifications herself or whether, perhaps, the children are hoping to surprise her by updating her wardrobe.

"They're amusing themselves all right – altering Grandma's dresses to seven inches above the knee."

Sunday Express, 24 April 1966

90 This was a period when a large number of young music groups released a wide range of "protest songs" associated with movements demanding social change, which obviously irritated Father and some of the older generations.

"Ultimatum from Dad – make that the last song about the mess his generation's put yours in."

Daily Express, 20 September 1966

Having left Plymouth on 29 January, it was reported that 65-year-old Francis Chichester was sailing home to finish the first West to East solo circumnavigation of the world, rounding Cape Horn on 3 March. He was made Sir Francis by the Queen later that summer for "individual achievement and sustained endeavour in the navigation and seamanship of small craft". His exploits inspired many people, including Father.

"Every year I hope he'll forget it, but every year someone like Sir Francis Chichester makes the headlines."

Sunday Express, 19 March 1967

The day before, in the Grand National Steeplechase, a mass pile-up of horses and jockeys at the 23rd fence caused a major upset to the race. Foinavon, an outsider with odds of 100–1, managed to avoid the melee and won the race. Obviously, Father's money was not on him.

"He couldn't have had much luck with football or the National yesterday – reckons his team ought to be conscripted to build a housing estate on the Aintree course."

Sunday Express, 9 April 1967

In this cartoon, Giles combines a popular British children's game with a major international political incident. Vera's newspaper refers to a period of great tension at the time due to the threat of a joint invasion of Czechoslovakia by four Warsaw Pact countries, which actually occurred three weeks later on the night of 20 August. Its aim was to crush the "Prague Spring" – a brief period of liberalisation in the then communist country, introduced by the country's First Secretary Alexander Dubček.

"I've put hundreds of 'em in Grandma's Guinness and they don't do her any harm."

Daily Express, 1 August 1968

94　The Government introduced a system of First Class and Second Class mail the following day, replacing the previous system of letters and printed papers. It aimed to deliver First Class post on the next working day after posting in most parts of the country. The cost of a stamp for a letter up to 4oz in weight was 5 pence for First Class and 4 pence for Second Class. As is often the case, in addition to illustrating Grandma's apparently unjustified anger at the increase, Giles has taken the opportunity to introduce a number of other incidental activities into the general scene.

"I don't know why she's 'ollering. She's never sent a letter with a stamp on yet."

Sunday Express, 15 September 1968

Three days after this cartoon appeared, there was a national strike of dock workers over a rejected pay claim, which started after
a long period of discussions and lasted for two and a half weeks. There was considerable concern that it would cause major
shortages of food throughout the country and a state of emergency was proclaimed. The neighbour's suspicions concerning
Grandma and Henrietta's sudden lack of production are correct.

"No I don't think Henrietta has gone off laying. I think someone next door has read about a dock strike and possible
food shortage."

Sunday Express, 12 July 1970

96 During the previous three days, a series of 21 letter bombs had been sent or addressed to the Israeli Embassy in London. The GPO was right to issue a general warning but perhaps Grandma is over-reacting a little, and to use poor little Vera in this way is a bit extreme.

"Grandma, it's not fair to send Vera all that way on her own to open your letters."

Daily Express, 22 September 1972

The following day was the Silver Wedding Anniversary of the marriage of the Queen and the Duke of Edinburgh. As part of the celebration, Prince Charles and Princess Anne organised an Anniversary Dinner at Buckingham Palace, and Giles was asked by them to provide a cartoon for the cover of the programme. Grandma, who I believe was the cartoonist's favourite family member, was chosen to appear on the cover.

"Daddy would be much happier if you didn't keep referring to 25 years ago as 'Medieval Times.'"

Sunday Express, 19 November 1972

98　In England, the summer holiday usually begins in late July and lasts for about six weeks. Mother was probably desperate to find something to occupy the children of the family but was not really expecting this.

"When I said build them a tree-house to keep them quiet, I didn't mean to include room service."

Sunday Express, 24 July 1977

Suffragettes were members of an activist women's organisation in the early 20th century who fought for the right of women to vote in public elections. Their actions included chaining themselves to railings. This cartoon appeared on the 50th anniversary of the 1928 Act, which gave all women over 21 years of age the right to vote regardless of property ownership. Prior to this, only women over 30 who met minimum property qualifications could vote. Unfortunately, in this celebration, it would seem that Grandma is not going to be released quickly.

"We chained Grandma up to celebrate the Suffragettes anniversary and Butch has swallowed the key."

Sunday Express, 2 July 1978

100　Even looking at all the various childish antics Giles has managed to include here, Grandma's comment is a bit strong. However, when that bag of flour explodes on her head, her suggestions regarding the children's future may be even more extreme.

"Dropping 'em all in a pool of piranha fish is not what Lord Justice Lawton had in mind when he called for a return to discipline and traditional moral standards."

Sunday Express, 3 September 1978

This was a time when cost cutting was being considered in the newspaper business and someone obviously felt that Grandma 101 was expendable. It is interesting to note that Ernie, Grandma's frequent adversary within the family, is busy writing what looks suspiciously like a letter.

"Who wrote to Lord Matthews and nominated me for first of the chops?"

Sunday Express, 27 July 1980

102 Mary Quant was an important 1960s London-based designer who pioneered the fashion for miniskirts and hotpants. This cartoon appeared at the time when she had her Autumn '81 collection on show in London. It is possible that Grandma was young once, but very difficult to imagine.

"Not in the wildest stretches of the imagination can I picture your Grandma wearing them in the 1920s."

Sunday Express, 24 May 1981

A gardening guide had just been released by the BBC entitled *Shirley Conran's Magic Garden*. The *Daily Express* must have picked up on it but this obviously did not impress Father.

"*Daily Express* 'witty guides to gardening for the total ignoramus' won't make me like it more than I do already."

Daily Express, 29 March 1983

Two days after the London Marathon and Father is still feeling the effects.

"Like last year, Butch, forget walkies for a few days after his marathon."

Daily Express, 15 May 1984

"I'd have thought you might let them get Guy Fawkes night over first."

Sunday Express, 4 November 1984

The 1985 Epsom Derby had been held the day before and won by Slip Anchor, ridden by American jockey Steve Cauthen. Obviously Grandma had placed her bet on Lester Piggott, a nine-time winner of the Derby who was expected to win, but finished far back in the field, hence her reaction. Piggott retired from jockeying at the end of that season and became a trainer.

"Mrs Thatcher would certainly give Grandma's State Benefits a radical overhaul if she knew they all went on Lester Piggott yesterday."

Daily Express, 6 June 1985

This was Giles's way of marking the Queen Mother's 85th birthday, and it looks as if Grandma is playing "Happy Birthday" back to front.

"Stop telling me the Queen Mother is twice my age and does her own garden and you bet it doesn't look a mess like ours."

Sunday Express, 4 August 1985

108 The Labour Party Annual Conference was taking place at Liverpool at this time. Derek Hatton, Deputy Leader of Liverpool City Council and member of the city's Militant Group, was expressing outspoken political views at the conference, obviously to Grandma's disapproval. She is suggesting some sort of physical retribution involving Hurricane Higgins, the iconic Northern Irish professional snooker player and Frank Bruno, the popular British boxer who won the World Heavyweight title ten years after this cartoon appeared.

"Grandma on politics...she'd give Hurricane Higgins 14 rounds in the ring with Frank Bruno, then send them both up to Liverpool to give Derek Hatton a hammering."

Daily Express, 3 October 1985

Martina Navratilova became one of the most dominant players in women's tennis at this time and was renowned for her powerful hard-hitting style of play. It looks as if Grandma is modelling her play upon her and it is obvious that poor Vera has already become a victim. The children are taking necessary precautions.

"Far corner, Martina Navratilova to serve – FORE."

Sunday Express, 5 July 1987

110   This was four days after the night of the Great Storm with hurricane-force winds causing casualties and considerable damage in the UK, France and the Channel Islands; the highest gusts reached 134 mph. Grandma has managed to find a way of making money out of the disaster.

"Grandma, we don't mind you helping the neighbours clear up their hurricane damage for a fiver, but we do mind you sweeping it into our garden."

Daily Express, 20 October 1987

"Every year we're not going to have this lark again – we're going to make our own snowplough. He's off to start one right now."

Sunday Express, 24 January 1988

112   Giles has used Ernie here to mark Leap Year and also to record that there was snow again. At the very end of February that year, temperatures dropped below zero.

"If Janice did propose to you I think we should wait a little while before we take out the licence."

Daily Express, 1 March 1988

Mother was four months too early. The Licensing Act 1988 changed public house opening times, requiring them to be closed for "4 hours beginning at 3.00 pm" instead of the previous "5 hours beginning at 2.00 pm". However, this did not come into force until 22nd August.

"I've made dinner for four o'clock – I thought your new three o'clock closing time law had started."

Sunday Express, 24 April 1988

The children have finally succeeded in achieving their aim regarding Grandma's hat – see cartoon dated 4 November 1984 in this chapter.

"Stand by for some real fireworks – Grandma's just found what's left of her hat you used on the guy."

Sunday Express, 6 November 1988

Three days earlier, the Health Minister Edwina Currie had provoked anger, particularly in the farming industry, by stating that most of Britain's egg production was infected by the salmonella bacterium.

"If Currie means it's going to save me this morning trip to collect one egg out of you bunch of layabouts then hooray for salmonella."

Daily Express, 6 December 1988

116   This was the start of the 1989 English cricket season, the 90th since the establishment of the English County Championship as an official competition. It is clear that not a great deal will be done this Sunday regarding the lawn. Stinker, the family's neighbour, is practicing his hunting skills with his bow.

"I like the smart uniform they're wearing to make their 'Really good start on the lawn this Sunday.'"

Sunday Express, 16 April 1989

Mother knows how to make a strong point, Ernie manages to break two windows with one ball, Grandma is immersed in the cricket news and Vera is reading about American tennis star Chris Evert announcing her retirement from the game.

"Like me to fill it in for you?"

Sunday Express, 9 July 1989

When Grandma's horse does not perform well, even the children are not safe. This was the day after the Grand National race when Docklands Express "jumped big, landed steeply and fell forward onto his face". Luckily he was not injured but, unfortunately, Grandma's money must have been on him. As Father's newspaper shows, Seagrass won the race.

"I told you not to trust her with the mower after her horse refused at the first fence."

Sunday Express, 7 April 1991

On Holiday

A good example of Giles's drawing ability, capturing a pretty Devon seaside village.

The strange desire of the British to paddle at least once a year. (Devon)

Daily Express, 21 August 1951

120 The Royal Meteorological Society reported that throughout the month of August, "As a holiday month it was disappointing in most districts, outdoor events being handicapped by the frequent days with rain". Giles is probably expressing his own thoughts with this cartoon.

"Marvellous, isn't it? Come here every year for my holidays and go back every year telling 'em I've had a wonderful time."
(Cornwall)

Daily Express, 29 August 1951

Another good example of Giles's drawing skills – his caravan, which appears in many of his holiday cartoons, can just be glimpsed on the left.

"Stand by for an acute attack of Grandma's deafness – I'm just going to tell her to get ready to go home."

Daily Express, 14 September 1954

122   Compare this cartoon with that dated 9 July 1958 in the chapter on Meal Times. A similar setting and theme, with a modified background and the various family members involved in different activities. The bull, however, has now been let into the group by a different child, which should cause a stir. Giles occasionally linked two cartoons, sometimes with years in between, as in the case here.

Daily Express, 1 June 1955

The Government was discussing the likelihood of coal shortages during the coming winter due, in part, to people not buying coal early enough and then creating a rush when the cold weather arrived. Father no doubt simply wishes to be left alone to enjoy the summer weather.

123

"That's a nice thing to say to Grandma when she asked you what our coal stock's like at home."

Sunday Express, 17 July 1955

Obviously not quite what the family was expecting.

"Oo said anything about peace and quiet? My advert said 'Seaside 'ut, 'arf- minute from sea, not another 'ouse for miles,' and nor there ain't."

Daily Express, 11 August 1955

Twelve days earlier, President Nasser of Egypt had announced the nationalisation of the Suez Canal Company. This British–French enterprise had owned and operated the Suez Canal since its construction in 1869 and the move was causing some concern regarding the British troops stationed in the country. August in Egypt can be very hot, especially in contrast to this summer in England when there was a freak hailstorm and snow, so it is questionable whether the balaclavas will be particularly welcomed by the troops.

"Lend us a couple of those balaclavas you're knitting for the troops, Vera."

Daily Express, 8 August 1956

126   Giles is making it clear that his cartoon family would feel very much at home in Ireland. This cartoon illustrates the pleasure Giles got from drawing a great mass of humanity.

Now they are setting off south – among the most Gile-ish people in the world.

Daily Express, 11 November 1958

Father is obviously not prepared to change his attire for a holiday in the sun.

127

"Here comes Father. Best case of 'Time-will-not-change-thee' I've ever met."

Daily Express, 18 May 1959

128   I suggest that the *Daily Express* could possibly have been prepared to include a picture of the oncoming impasse but very much doubt that the BBC would have been happy to broadcast Grandma's thoughts on the subject.

"We'll sell the picture to the *Express* and Grandma's comments on sailing to the BBC."

Daily Express, 6 June 1960

Looking at the weather, Father is understandably keen to avoid the trip by persuading the ferryman to join the seaman's strike taking place at the time. The location for this cartoon is Felixstowe Ferry on the River Deben in Suffolk, close to Giles's home. The ferryman is Charlie Brinkley, a good friend of the cartoonist, who appears in a number of his cartoons.

"Can you and me reach a pay-agreement with a condition that you join the seamen's strike immediately?"

Sunday Express, 14 August 1960

Giles has captured a typical Italian townscape in this cartoon but the crowd appears bemused by the weird commentary on the cricket match taking place between England and Australia in Leeds. England won by eight wickets.

"Davidson sends down a Chinaman – Subba Row plays it to silly mid-off, through the covers to the boundary for four, but the umpire has signalled 'No ball', etc., etc...."

Sunday Express, 9 July 1961

To be fair, Father is rather heavily laden down and New York Zoo on a warm Sunday afternoon does require a certain amount of stamina. Maybe the family should have left him behind. This is another example illustrating Giles's love of drawing great crowds of people.

"Well, I DON'T think a nice Sunday walk round the New York Zoo is doing me more good than snoring my head off in an armchair at home."

Sunday Express, 30 September 1962

Grandma's penchant for speaking her mind has got her in trouble again.

"Dad! You know Grandma said she'd like to tell one of these cops what she thinks of them before we went home?"

Daily Express, 5 October 1962

This cartoon, set in the Mersey Tunnel in Liverpool, shows Giles's Land Rover LRT 140 and his caravan/travelling studio. The policeman is a little out-of-date as the day before, Hailsham Hogg, 2nd Viscount Hailsham renounced his peerage and became Quintin Hogg. The Government at that time was discussing the proposal to make the fitting of safety belts compulsory in all new cars.

"We are going to need Mr. Ailsham 'Ogg's better roads if your little lad's going to keep losing his ball during rush hours."

Daily Express, 28 November 1963

This cartoon shows Giles's caravan/touring studio with Blackpool's famous tower in the background. It also includes two of Grandma's numerous female siblings.

"Stand by for a fab bout of Blackpool hospitality, daddyo – here come two of Grandma's northern sisters."

Daily Express, 2 December 1963

During the previous month there had been a series of airline hijackings. Poor Vera was particularly susceptible to pills.

"Psst! Lady – want any anti-hijack pills, ten dollars a dozen?"

Daily Express, 8 October 1970

There had been a number of reports over the years about pilots falling asleep mid-flight but Grandma's solution may equally distract the pilot from his duties.

"I don't think our Captain will doze off – I've just slipped a couple of my Laxitivo Pills in his tea."

Daily Express, 14 December 1972

The Giles family was very unlucky with its choice of holiday destination. Weather reports for that month state, "Such places as North Wales and N. W. England had about double their normal rainfall", whereas in Eastern Scotland, East Anglia and S. W. England "rainfall totals were 50% of average or less".

"As a matter of fact we do not think this is better than taking one of those chancy holidays in the Med."

Sunday Express, 28 July 1974

138 The village in the background is Pin Mill near Ipswich, on the River Orwell and only a few miles from Giles's home. He would have sailed many times on this stretch of water and often quenched his thirst in the Butt and Oyster public house shown in the background near the Thames barges. The family has chosen a very bad time of the year to try out their new acquisition, presumably just bought at the Earls Court Boat Show earlier that month.

"Funny, it looked much bigger at the Boat Show."

Sunday Express, 12 January 1975

Following the 1975 Cricket World Cup, the Australian cricket team stayed to play a four-match Test series against England. The English team was broadly unable to withstand the pace-bowling of the visitors who won the series 1–0, with three matches drawn, and therefore retained The Ashes.

"That's how the Aussies do it – bowl 'em on the feet, make 'em hop out of their crease, and BINGO!!"

Daily Express, 13 June 1975

140 Shortly before this cartoon appeared, a beached whale, stranded at Clacton, was saved by a group of boys by pouring sea water on it until help could arrive.

"It keeps them amused – they read about those boys who revived a whale with pails of cold water."

Daily Express, 29 July 1975

In the summer that year, the country experienced a heatwave with very high temperatures being recorded and severe drought experienced in many areas. Unfortunately at the end of August, when the family had booked its holiday, severe thunderstorms brought rain to some areas for the first time in weeks.

"Remember the hysterical laughter when I said 'Do we want to take our rain coats'?"

Sunday Express, 29 August 1976

142   Mother is right to admonish Father for taking out his misery on the unfortunate theme park attendant for the loss by his football team the previous day, compounded by the awful weather.

"Stop calling him that every time we come past – it's not his fault your team lost their first game!"

Sunday Express, 24 August 1986

This cartoon refers to The Brink's-Mat robbery which occurred at the Heathrow International Trading Estate in November 1983. £26 million worth of gold bullion was stolen from a warehouse, the majority of which has never been recovered. Two days before this cartoon appeared, a lawyer was convicted for helping launder some of the proceeds from the robbery and was sentenced to 12 years in prison.

"They're paying in gold bullion for six vanilla cornets and they want £24,997.60 change."

Sunday Express, 10 July 1988

144   Father has obviously decided to duck out of this holiday – a decision possibly based on past experiences. Grandma, as usual, is not behaving herself and at the same time is studying a racing journal.

"This isn't Dad – it's a straw-packed dummy!"

Sunday Express, 26 March 1989

The Royal Family

At this time, Prince Philip had commented on television that he was worried about the royal family's expenses. It is recorded that he added, "If nothing happens – I don't know – we may have to move to smaller premises."

"Nothing gets on my nerves more than a bailiff whistling Elgar's 'Pomp and Circumstance.'"

Daily Express, 11 November 1969

146   The Government was discussing the possibility of rent rebates for council tenants and obviously there were still some concerns about finances in Buckingham Palace.

"I hardly feel, dear, that because the sink at Balmoral hasn't been working properly since your great-great-grandmother's time, it justifies claiming a rent rebate."

Daily Express, 5 November 1970

It was reported that Prince Philip was always very security conscious.

"Careful what you spend, dear – third vase back row on your left."

Daily Express, 25 February 1975

Prince Edward is the Queen's third son and was aged 11 when this cartoon appeared. Perhaps the phone call was from a girl friend in America who had forgotten to take the five-hour time difference into account.

"Remind me to have a word with Edward about his girl friends phoning the Palace at two in the morning."

Daily Express, 13 January 1976

Princess Anne's then husband, Captain Mark Phillips, is referring to comments made by Prince Philip a few days earlier in which he had compared Britain's economic troubles to the spread of dry rot in a building.

"I see Daddy's set the fur flying again, Anne. Your turn next."

Sunday Express, 20 January 1977

150   There had been some confusion about the attribution of paintings between the English landscape artist John Constable and his son. Obviously Prince Philip did not wish there to be any similar confusion about the creator of his son's efforts.

"Now you've taken up art, Charles, please pay special attention to the signature and avoid the same confusion as Constable and his son."

Sunday Express, 8 October 1978

This was the day of the State Opening of Parliament – there is little danger of the Queen experiencing the embarrassment of someone else wearing the same headgear.

"At least there's no danger of the ladies wearing the same hats today."

Daily Express, 15 May 1979

No doubt nobody wanted to win this honour.

"We're poker dicing for who takes HRH the first revealing instalment of 'Philip' in the *Daily Express*, Your Majesty."

Daily Express, 23 September 1980

Zara, being put on the horse, is the daughter of Princess Anne and Captain Mark Phillips and was born two days before this cartoon appeared. Their family home, Gatcombe Park, appears in the background. Not surprisingly, Zara has grown up to be a "natural horsewoman".

"One can't start too early."

Sunday Express, 17 May 1981

On an official visit to Australia, Princess Diana insisted on taking along nine-month-old Prince William. This cartoon illustrates Giles's joy and skill at drawing, in very accurate detail, a wide range of official uniforms.

Daily Express, 12 March 1983

"Permission to remove tomahawk from birthday present, Ma'am? HRH has already scalped the butler, the first footman, the second cook..."

Daily Express, 21 June 1983

156 Prince William was 18 months old when this cartoon appeared. His father, Prince Charles, had taken it all in good humour when, two days earlier, a custard pie was thrown at his face as a joke on a visit to a Sport and Social Club in Manchester.

"But, Charles – you were laughing when that girl threw a custard pie at you!"

Daily Express, 22 December 1983

The day before, Princess Diana had officially announced that she was expecting her second child. Seven months later, Prince Harry was born on 15 September.

"Diana – where did you put William's old pram?"

Daily Express, 14 February 1984

The Queen and Prince Philip were on a visit to the Hashemite Kingdom of Jordan amid tight security.

"Peace be with you, Ma'am, they're some of ours. Mixture of King Hussein's bodyguard and the S.A.S."

Daily Express, 27 March 1984

Prince William is giving vent to his feelings and Prince Harry appears to be enjoying the whole thing. Alf Garnett was a main character (played by Warren Mitchell) in the very popular TV programme *'Till Death Us Do Part*, and the character was famous for his robust and outspoken outbursts. The character Alf Garnett appeared in a number of Giles's cartoons and Warren Mitchell was a good friend of the cartoonist in real life.

159

"That wasn't from Bergerac – I think Wills got that one from Alf Garnett."

Sunday Express, 13 October 1985

British Cartoon Archive

All the cartoons in this book were copied from material in Carl Giles's own private archive, a huge collection of artwork, ephemera and correspondence, which is held by the British Cartoon Archive at the University of Kent. Carl Giles had been cartoonist for Lord Beaverbrook's *Daily* and *Sunday Express* for almost 20 years, when on 20 March 1962 the Conservative M.P. Sir Martin Lindsay tabled a motion deploring "the conduct of Lord Beaverbrook in authorizing over the last few years in the newspapers controlled by him more than 70 adverse comments on members of the royal family who have no means of replying".

Lindsay was wrong about the royal family having no means of reply. That day Prince Philip also vented his anger at Beaverbrook's campaign, during a press reception at the British Embassy in Rio de Janeiro. According to the paper's Brazil representative, the Prince declared that, "The *Daily Express* is a bloody awful newspaper. It is full of lies, scandal and imagination. It is a vicious paper."

When the *Daily Express* reported this the next day, Giles decided to treat it as a joke. He knew the royal family enjoyed his cartoons; they often asked for the artwork. This had begun in 1948, when Prince Philip was sent a cartoon on the State Opening of Parliament, and over the next few years Giles received a steady stream of requests from Buckingham Palace for original drawings.

Left: *Lord Beaverbrook is marched to the Tower, 22 March 1962.*

Giles drew the diminutive Lord Beaverbrook being escorted through the Traitor's Gate at the Tower of London, with a headsman's axe and block standing ready in the background. The caption repeated Prince Philip's condemnation of the *Daily Express*, but added laconically: "'Ah well,' said Lord B., as they trotted him off to the Tower, 'at least he takes it or he wouldn't know it was a bloody awful newspaper.'"

This was a brilliant response, which did much to defuse the situation. When Giles's cartoon was printed the next day, *Daily Express* staff were surprised to receive a phone call from the Queen's press secretary, with a message for Giles that "Her Majesty requests today's cartoon to commemorate one of her husband's most glorious indiscretions."

Giles sent off the artwork and in May 1962 found himself invited to "a small informal luncheon party" at Buckingham Palace with the Queen and Prince Philip. "I was filled with absolute dread," Giles recalled afterwards. "But as soon as she started to talk I was put at my ease…There were about half a dozen corgis running about in a completely uncontrolled state. Suddenly the Queen shouted, 'HEP'. It was like a bark from a sergeant major. The corgis immediately stood to attention. Then filed out of the room."

After the lunch Giles mischievously drew a cartoon of the guests leaving with corgi-savaged trousers. He sent it to the Queen, who returned her thanks through one of her private secretaries, noting that she was "glad that you got away without having lost, at least to the best of her knowledge, so much as a shred of your trousers".

After that Giles became what one *Daily Express* journalist called "a kind of cartooning jester to the royal family". By the time he retired in 1991, the royal family had more than 40 of his original drawings, the largest number being owned by Prince Philip, who shared Giles's anarchic view of the world.

The British Cartoon Archive, based at the University of Kent's Templeman Library in Canterbury, is dedicated to the history of British cartooning over the last two hundred years. It holds the artwork for more than 150,000 British political and social-comment cartoons, plus large collections of comic strips, newspaper cuttings, books and magazines. Its website at www.cartoons.ac.uk has over 200,000 cartoon images, including the majority of Carl Giles's published work.